FOREWC

The ten stories that follow start
entertainment for my elderly mother. vvnen i wao
a child, however much I pleaded with my parents, they
wouldn't let me have a dog, there was always a plausible
excuse. Their mantra at the time was, 'when you get married
and have a home of your own you can have as many dogs
as you like, I'm sure that they didn't think for one
second, that I would have so many. As it turned out
they loved all of my dogs and took pleasure in their company.

Between the years 1965 and 2006 I owned the grand total
of 14 dogs and 35 puppies. They amounted to 8 Dalmatians,
4 Afghan Hounds, 1 Doberman, 1 scruffy muttley and
35 Dalmatian puppies, all of which I loved dearly.
William Blake was just that little bit special and a highly
intelligent being.

I have been asked how William Blake came by his name,
that was my daughters idea. Nickname, Willy Bumble
came from me, it just seemed to suit him. However, you
will read about his adventure with a bumble-bee in the
next set of stories of William's misdemeanours. His kennel
name was Duxfordham William.

During the mid 1960's and 70's when these stories are set
it was very different way of life, it was a much freer society
and it was acceptable that dogs went out on their own to
roam. William Blake really was the village dog. For William,
the most important things in life were food, fun, sleep,
adventures and copious amounts of love for all, not
necessarily in that order.

I hope you find William Blakes adventures amusing, he really
was my bestest ever friend.

Patricia. x

The Misdemeanours of William Blake

These stories have been written, first of all
with my elderly mother in mind and secondly
for anyone who wants a nice gentle read
with a little bit of humour thrown in
and who loves dogs.

I hope you enjoy reading them as much
as I have enjoyed writing them.

Much love Dottie x

First published in Great Britain 2019

Republished in 2020 by Janus Publishing Company Ltd
The Studio
High Green
Great Shelford
Cambridge CB22 5EG

www.januspublishing.co.uk

ISBN: 978-1-85756-915-5

Printed and bound in Great Britain

Contents

In the beginning   1

The Fair   7

The Pond   15

New Neighbours   19

The Seaside   25

Christmas   33

The Mini   41

The Thief   47

The Birthday   53

Down the Road   61

Acknowledgments   67

We must go and see the puppies tomorrow...

In the Beginning

7 Dog Kennel Lane
Pidley
Cambridge
CB30 4WB

Dear Friends,

What a lovely day in September for a wedding. The sun shone, the church was full with all our relatives and friends and everything went well. I was very young, only seventeen. So it was quite a leap into the unknown for such a young person.

The one thing I did know that I wanted, as soon as possible, was a dog. I had plagued the life out of my parents for years, but they wouldn't let me have one. The answer was always the same, when you get married and have a home of your own, you can have as many as you like. So I did, but I'll tell you all about that at a later date. For now, I wasn't going to waste any time in fulfilling my dream. My husband Greg and I had discussed the subject many times. Greg wasn't too sure about having a dog. His mother was frightened of them and a little bit of that had rubbed off on him. I had always been keen on owning a dog, and I was desperate to have one. I spent some time reassuring Greg it would be OK. Eventually he said. "Alright we'll give it a try." I was very excited and wanted to get my dog, before Greg changed his mind.

A magical warm tender feeling engulfed my whole being

Now it was only a question of which type of dog to choose. We looked at several breeds over the next few weeks. Then one day an advert in the local paper caught my eye. I was trembling with excitement, "We must go and see the puppies tomorrow," I said. So I rang and made a mutually agreeable time to go and see them. We were to go at 6 o'clock the next evening.

I was spell-bound from the outset. A magical warm tender feeling engulfed my whole being, I tingled from head to toe as I gazed down at the puppies. I wonder if you can guess what I was looking at. I can tell you that they were snow white, seven with little black noses and four with brown noses.

Their father was a big strong dog called Arthur. He was white with black spots and their mother who was called Rachel, was white with brown spots. Now you have it, yes they were a litter of Dalmatians. It was love at first sight. They were quite adorable, beautiful and very cuddly.

Incidentally, did you know, the spots appear when the puppies are about ten days old. They cannot leave their mothers until they are at least eight weeks old, so by the time the puppy would come to live with us, he or she would have all or at least, most of their spots.

William leapt to his feet and disappeared

I asked the owner if it would be alright if I climbed in to the whelping box. She gave me a rather strange look, but agreed that I could. I carefully sat in the corner of the box and let the puppies crawl all over me. It was lovely, they were very soft and cuddly and that puppy smell was just awesome. I know you must be thinking, what a strange woman. Well, I suppose I am. However, it let me get up close and personal with them. There was one little puppy with a spotty nose, and velvet ears, who was very inquisitive. He chewed my fingers and licked my face and was generally very, very friendly. Oh how I loved him. I cradled him in my arms and stroked his little head. He looked up at me lovingly with his big brown eyes.

I saw a white waggy tail disappearing out of the gateway

Well, that did it, "This is the one," I said. I just had to have him. None of the others would do. It was strange, we had a mutual attraction for each other, right from that very first time of meeting. So 'William' as we named him, came to live with us, when he was just ten weeks old. He grew very quickly, and was always hungry and full of mischief.

One day the gate was left open and without a second thought, William leapt to his feet and disappeared. I saw a white waggy tail disappearing out of the gateway. He was gone in a flash, with me yelling my head off, "William sit, William come here! William will you do as you are told!"

Then there was an awful sound, the screeching of brakes, and a horrible thud. My heart was in my mouth, I thought William had been run over. Before I had time to collect myself and react, William came rushing round the corner and jumped into my arms whimpering and shaking. Fortunately, although he had been hit by a car, it had only bruised him on his rear end.

I went in and cuddled him and told him, I loved him

He whimpered and shook in my arms for a good five minutes. As I cuddled him, I realised how close I had come to losing him and gave him a big hug. Eventually, he struggled to get down and sloped off to his bed as though nothing had happened.

What a lucky dog! I was so angry with him. I didn't know whether to be cross and smack him or scold him. As I was still in shock myself, I went in and cuddled him and told him, I loved him.

When Greg came home, I sat him down and told him of the day's events. "We must make sure the gate is closed at all times" I said. Greg agreed and said he would do his best to make sure William didn't escape again. As you will find out at a future date we were not always successful.

William was fast asleep in his bed when I went to see him, just before going upstairs to bed myself. I stroked his little head and he lifted one blurry eye and gave a little moan. I gave him a kiss on his head and whispered in his ear.

"You must learn all about the traffic, sooner rather than later."

And there's more...
Much love Dottie.

The Fair

7 Dog Kennel Lane
Pidley
Cambridge
CB30 4WB

Dear Friends,

William settled in and lived with us quite happily as a member of our family team. Now that I had achieved getting my first dog, I was contemplating getting another, when life took over and I found that I was pregnant with my second child. I gave birth to a son, a brother for Vicky my daughter. So now we were a team. Greg and I, Vicky, Matt and William.

 A few years passed and my ambition to have more dogs had to go on hold for a while. I secretly had already made up my mind to get William a wife... but I waited until the time was right and

William was still in disguise as a Zebra...

that I would get agreement from the team...

William was so good with the children and quite frankly I suppose I felt I had three children, even if one had spots and four legs. They all grew up very happily together.

William went everywhere with them, except school. (now there's a tale for another time) So as time went on it was no surprise to me that they went on adventures together. It was an exciting day, as the fair had come to the village. There were lots of amusements, a ghost train, a moving staircase, dodgems, stalls where you could win a prize, and a shooting gallery and lots more.

The children decided just to enjoy themselves

William and the children were full of excitement and at last it was time to go and join in the fun!! They hitched William to his lead and off they went. William was very excited and pulled on his lead all the way. He had plans! As soon as they reached the fairground, William slipped his lead and ran off into the crowd. As there was little or no chance of catching him, the children decided just to enjoy themselves and if they saw William then they would try to hitch him to his lead.

The lady who was offering the face painting, had given William a makeover. He was now in disguise as a Zebra. They will never catch me now he thought. (The fact that he still had a spotted body had escaped him). He really liked being a Zebra as everyone patted him and made a fuss of him.

Next on his list was the ghost train, he hopped into a carriage and off it sped, horrible frightening screams, skeletons rattled as he went by and cob webs draped themselves all around him. He wasn't too sure he liked this.

He could hear people clapping and shouting "Well done William!"

When eventually it came to an end, he jumped off the carriage very quickly, shaking all over and was very wobbly on his feet. On a score of one to ten, he rated it at minus ten.

He went off to see if he could find something more entertaining, The helter skelter looked like fun. He climbed the stairs to the top and sat on a mat. A gentle push from the next person in the line and he was off. Careering down, twisting and turning until he hit the bottom. A little stunned, he could hear people clapping and shouting "Well done William!".

That was fun he thought, now where shall I go. A man called to him from a carousel. On it there were horses that went up and down. "Come on William I'll take you for a ride with the horses". William jumped up, but as he couldn't sit on a horse, he decided to position himself between the horses legs.

A friendly girl offered him a lick of her toffee apple

Eventually, the ride started, it went round and round and round. William felt very odd. All the people standing watching were just a blur and he felt very sick. "You don't look too good my friend", said the man, as he pulled William on to the centre of the stand. "Don't worry I'll stop the ride and you can get off. Poor old chap," said the man as William stumbled off the ride. It took a few minutes for him to recover from this experience. A friendly girl offered him a lick of her toffee apple, because as she said, "This will make you feel better William". Well It would have been rude not to accept. Ten seconds later, with the toffee apple totally devoured, and William licking his lips, he ran and off in pursuit of another adventure.

What next, I know I'll go and have my fortune read, perhaps she will tell me that I'm going to find and nice big juicy bone. He sat in front of a very pretty lady with a beautiful smile, she began to tell William that she could see a long lead with a shiny clip on it, he was hooked, quite literally.

"Didn't we have a brilliant time" said Matt

The children had caught up with him and clipped on his lead. He was well and truly caught! (Until the next time that is) Vicky, Matt and William set off home for tea. They agreed between themselves not say too much about William's exploits at the fair that afternoon. "Didn't we have a brilliant time," said Matt, "Oh, it really was good," said Vicky and I know William enjoyed himself too. When they arrived home, William was still in disguise as a Zebra. Which brought about many, many questions from me. In about 15 minutes I had extracted all that had happened during the afternoon. I couldn't stop laughing and when I tried to tell Greg, the tears streamed down my face with laughter...

"Oh and there's another thing I spluttered, William's been given a surname. It's 'Blake'..."Oh that makes him sound very important. Where on earth did that come from", asked Greg. "I'm not too sure", I said. Vicky announced it when she came back from the fair. So William Blake it is.

And there's more...
Much love Dottie.

I had just shampooed William nicely...

The Pond

7 Dog Kennel Lane
Pidley
Cambridge
CB30 4WB

Dear Friends,

It was summer time when the days were long and the weather was sunny and warm. William was very fond of a nice long walk, preferably off his lead. So one warm summer evening, Greg my husband and I our two children Matt, Vicky and William, (on his lead) set off for a pleasant long walk. Well, that was the intention. We might have known better, no walk with William was ever that straight forward

We took to the fields, where we could let William off his lead. It was a delight to watch him run. Every now and again he would stop, jump high in the air and have a good look round to see if we were within his sight.

About an hour into our walk, we came across a water mill. It had a big pond with a river running into it at one end. There was a beautiful pair of swans and assorted ducks swimming about minding their own business. It was truly an idyllic sight. William was fascinated by these creatures, he didn't know what to make of them. One thing he did know was that he wanted to get closer, so he could give them a great big sniff.

Secretly I found it quite amusing

The problem was that William hated water. He didn't like the rain, and puddles he walked around, and as far as a bath was concerned, that was a definite No—No! He ran up and down the bank trying to work out a way to reach the swans and ducks. He really couldn't fathom it out, when suddenly, he lost his footing and slipped on the mud, right into the pond. William started to panic, you see he couldn't swim. The swans were quite interested in this hullabaloo and came to investigate. William was very muddy and wet and extremely slippery.

The swans flapped their big wings and started to make a loud hissing noise. They were not happy about this dog entering their space. Every time he tried to get out, William slipped back on the mud. Well that did it, with Swans hissing and flapping and William howling, Greg waded into the pond and just managed to get hold of his collar and pull him out.

The children were laughing at him, (which William hated), he was covered in mud and weeds and didn't smell very nice. William slunk across to the children and can you guess what he did next? He shook from head to toe, several times, so whilst he was getting drier, the children were getting wetter.

"William Blake, you are such a naughty boy!" I said, a little tongue in cheek, secretly I found it quite amusing. We all made our way home covered in pond water and weeds and William smelt even worse with the evening sun drying him out. Arriving home it was baths all round, William couldn't believe it, not more water! Well what a performance, I put his front legs in the bath and oh how he wriggled. Eventually, I managed to persuade him to put his back legs in, I had just shampooed William nicely when he took a leap towards the open window (I forgot to say we were upstairs in the bathroom) I yelled, "No! No! William Blake just you settle down! "If you leap out of the window...", I didn't finish the sentence because I needed all my energy to hold onto him, he was as you can imagine very slippery.

With a great big tug he fell back into the bath. I quickly shut the window and once more proceeded to wash him. As I knew from experience I had to be very, very, quick with the towel. You know from the earlier incident what would happen next if I didn't wrap him up very quickly. I wrapped him firmly in a towel, with only his nose poking out. I rubbed and rubbed and after a short while I released my grip and he was off, racing down the stairs several at a time. Secretly, he was proud of his clean state and went to find Vicky and Matt for a cuddle.

All ended well and we went to bed. Everyone was very tired and we slept for ages.

And there's more...
Much love Dottie.

New Neighbours

7 Dog Kennel Lane
Pidley
Cambridge
CB30 4WB

Dear Friends,

It's always a bit unnerving when new neighbours move in next door. You're never quite sure whether you will get on. We were particularly nervous with a certain family member. I'm sure you've guessed the one, yes that's the one I mean, the one with four legs and spots. Well one sunny Saturday, that's exactly what happened. I desperately hoped they would be very special people, tolerant and understanding. They would need to be living next door to William. A large van drew up outside the house and from the outset, William was totally fascinated, watching through the sitting room window he could

I was pleased it was only a small dog...

see everything. About eleven o'clock, I went out and asked the new neighbours, if they would like a coffee break, it was so good to chat and get to know one another. I was relieved that they were so friendly. During the conversation, I learned that they had two sons and a dog. William's ears stood up on end. "What type," I asked politely, "Oh he's a Jack Russell called Sparky" came the reply. I was pleased it was only a small dog, however, I suppose I should have realised then, with a name like Sparky what might lie ahead.

William and Sparky were not going to be friends

It took most of the day to unload their household effects and William was curious about what was happening. He made sure he watched everything, from the kitchen table to the bed.

In fact, I had to call him in twice for getting in the way. Eventually, they settled in and as time went by, it was becoming obvious, that William and Sparky were not going to be friends.

One day, William was out in the garden, playing

with his nice shiny red ball, when he heard an awful yapping sound coming from the other side of the fence, he went over to investigate.

It was his new neighbour Sparky. Well, a hell of a ruckus ensued, I don't speak dog, but I can say, if it were human talk, it would have been very blue. William was very cross and so was Sparky. There was a howl from William, Sparky had caught William's nose with his sharp claws and there was a trickle of bright red blood running down it. "Oh William Blake" I cried, "do come in and I'll bathe it for you." I sat William on a chair and went to get my first aid kit.

After a while it stopped bleeding, but it was sore, "You won't be able to go sniffing around for a while. Now just you listen to me" I said in a stern voice, "Sparky obviously doesn't want to be friends, so just you leave him well alone." I found I was waving my finger, something my father had said not to do when I was a child, I quickly stopped and pretended that I hadn't done it.

Then one day the gate was left open, William crept through very quietly.., now he thought.., I'm going to sort that Sparky out once and for all. He pushed the neighbours gate open very gently and there was Sparky looking intently under the fence. William crept up slowly and suddenly pounced on Sparky, he grabbed him by the nape of his neck holding him high and waving him in the air. William was thinking what he might do next, Sparky was wriggling and growling for all he was worth. William carried him over to the wall and began to bash Sparky against it, just like an old carpet, what a racket.

I had visions of the most macabre kind

The growling and spitting was getting louder by the minute, Sparky's owner rushed round to my house and banged loudly on my front door. "Come quickly!" she yelled, "William has got Sparky by the throat," I ran round to her house as fast as I could, I had visions of the most macabre kind. By the time I reached the scene Sparky's eyes were popping out of his head and foam was billowing from his mouth. "William Blake!" I shouted, "put Sparky down." William being William, just had to do one more bash, I was so cross with him and I was very worried about what was going through my neighbours mind.

Eventually, William put Sparky down and I don't think I have ever seen William move so fast. He shot out of the garden, back into our house and into his basket, so by the time Sparky had regained his composure William was long gone. Sparky was bruised and sore but apart from that, all was well. I was trying to apologise to my neighbour as she was comforting Sparky in her arms, but I found that I had to shout because Sparky was making so much noise. He was growling and spitting, he was clearly very, very angry, he just wasn't having any of it. He wriggled and wriggled, he was desperate to get his own back, I left making a mental note to go back and apologise properly when Sparky had calmed down.

Was this the end of the story between William and Sparky, well, what do you think?

And there's more...

Much love Dottie.

The Seaside

7 Dog Kennel Lane
Pidley
Cambridge
CB30 4WB

Dear Friends,

The children had been asking me to take them to the seaside. They kept on and on, as only children can do. So one day during the school holidays I gave in, I invited two of their friends to join us and we packed up the car with buckets and spades and a picnic, "Don't forget William," they called out, "Of course not," I replied, I sat him in his seat in the car, settled the children in their seats and off we went. The weather was lovely and sunny, not a cloud in the sky, a glorious day for the seaside.

It took about an hour to reach the sea, so it was not a long way, but it was far enough with

William started to investigate a crab...

four excited children and a spotted dog. Eventually, as we turned a corner, a great chorus went up in the back of the car. "I can see the seaee... I can see the seaee," with a great deal of excitement and clunking of buckets and spades and calls of, "I need the loo!" I pulled into the beach car park. The children all made their way to the loo and William sorted himself out with a convenient post that was nearby. We gathered back at the car where I proceeded to issue my instructions for the day. "Don't go too far out, stay together, make sure you can see me at all times." So off we went with our clutter to find a good spot on the beach.

The children ran off to see who could reach the sea first

For William, it was his first experience of the seaside. He ran down onto the beach where he was confronted with sand, a strange feeling under my feet, he thought, what was this stuff? It felt slightly wet, he sniffed it and of course some stuck to his nose, still, never mind, it must be good stuff, because the children love it.

We found a place to settle with all our things and the children ran off to see who could reach the sea first. William barked and ran along with them. He was so excited, he ran off in front of the children and then it suddenly dawned on him, he dug his heels in and came to an abrupt halt, just before an incoming wave broke along the shore. Oh no, its water, lots and lots of it! He was horrified. He hated water, he even hated the thought of water, except for drinking.

He found his feet off the ground and the sea water coming closer

By this time the children had overtaken him and they all splashed around happily, "come on William," they shouted, William ran up and down barking his head off, wagging his tail he was happy just to watch and bark. Then, he saw the children whispering to each other, I wonder what that's all about he thought, they are definitely up to something, before he had time to ponder this thought the children had come out of the water and were patting him on his head and generally making a fuss of him.

This is nice he thought, when suddenly he found his feet off the ground and the sea water coming closer by the second, Oh No! I'm going to get really wet he thought. He wriggled up his nose and shuddered at the thought. Splosh! and the children dropped him into the sea. It was funny stuff, it tasted quite nice, not at all like bath water or puddles. The children all laughed at him which William hated, I'll get my own back he thought, just you wait and see.

He ran over to the children and had a good shake

Eventually, he decided to play with the children in spite of the water. They had a ball and a Frisbee they were throwing, so William had a lot of fun retrieving them. After a while, they decided that they were hungry so they all came running up the beach and descended on me and the rug, on which I had laid out food and drinks. "Go over there, all of you and brush off that water and sand,. Yes, you as well William, No! William Blake, don't you dare shake anywhere near me." He gave me one of his mischievous looks. I quickly moved away. "You won't get any food," I scolded. He thought better of it and that perhaps he wouldn't do it, not when there was food at stake. With that he ran over to the children and had a good shake, covering them with sea water and sand, I swear I saw him grin. William was satisfied now that he had got his own back for dropping him in the sea. Laughing and barking, what a happy time they were all having, they all came and sat on the rug and ate a hearty picnic.

The crab had attached itself to his nose

"You can have about another hour" I said, "how about collecting some stones and shells?" William really enjoyed this, as it involved lots of sniffing. He found some very curious things to sniff, "stay away from that!" yelled Matt, as William started to investigate a crab. Too late, the crab had attached itself to his nose and given him a nasty pinch. William was just about to retaliate in some way, he hadn't quite decided what that should be, when he felt a hand on his collar pulling him away. "No, I don't think so, come on lets go and find a big stone to

take home, I'll write your name on it if you're good"
said Matt. William licked his sore nose and off they
went. We all piled back in the car for the journey
home. "I noticed a cafe on the way here, how would
you like to stop for ice cream and Coca-Cola," I
said. Everyone agreed that this was a good plan.
When we arrived it was ice cream and Coca-Cola
all round including one for William.

Out came another explosion of great magnitude

We all made for the garden and I was pleasantly
surprised at how quiet they all were, I think the
sea air and all the running about had tired them
out, so it was very peaceful, almost tranquil. Then
from nowhere came great big burp, "William Blake,
how could you?," I said "It's rude to burp". He
looked dolefully at me, then he opened his mouth
and out came another explosion of great magnitude.
I really couldn't keep a straight face, I laughed
out loud, so did the children and all the people
in the garden were laughing as well. "Poor old
William," said Vicky "it must be the Coca-Cola".
"Please pardon my dog", I said to anyone that

was listening. We continued our journey home without any more incidents, the children couldn't wait to tell their father about the day's activities and especially Williams burps.

And there's more...

Much love Dottie.

Christmas

7 Dog Kennel Lane
Pidley
Cambridge
CB30 4WB

Dear Friends,

It was December the 24th only one day to go before Christmas Day and we were all very busy. There seemed to be an awful lot to do. The excitement was growing and William and the children were finding it hard to be good. They had to keep reminding themselves only good Children and Dogs received presents on Christmas Day.

William wasn't too sure what presents he would like to have. He started to mentally list them. Now a new collar and lead in Red, a cover for his bed, in Red, he thought would be nice, Oh yes he'd love a new ball, in Red, so it could be easily seen.

William was woken up by the lovely smells of food...

Last of all he would love a big juicy bone with a Red ribbon. Whilst he was thinking about all these lovely things, he nodded off in his basket with Christmas Carols serenading his slumber.

I was busy cooking. Surely I must have done enough by now!! With mince pies and sausage rolls, a big joint of boiled ham and to top it all, I had made a Christmas cake. I thought it would be fun to decorate the cake with lots of snow icing and put a little Dalmatian hiding in the snow, on the top. I would find out in due course if the others thought the same.

He sniffed the air and his mouth began to water

Matt was first to come into the kitchen. "Wow! that's fantastic," he exclaimed as he looked over the cake. "I'm sure William will be chuffed. You know he'll expect a piece now!" "I'm sure a small piece won't hurt him, I said and carried on with my organising of everything for tomorrow.

William was woken up by lovely smells of food. He sniffed the air and his mouth began to water.

"Oh WILLIAM BLAKE," I cried, "you're drooling again. It's horrid and it goes everywhere". "Oh Yuk", said Vicky, "it's a horrible habit you have. Don't you know it looks quite revolting". William was quite unmoved by her comments. He had heard them many times before. He gave her a quick nuzzle and wiped off the worst of the drool on her jeans. Vicky couldn't help but laugh as she went off to change her clothes.

William was full of expectation

The smell of the cooking had obviously caught Williams attention and he fancied a taste of something, or may be everything. "Very well," I said, "you can have a small piece of ham, then you MUST stop drooling". With his eyes wide open and strings of drool oozing from his mouth, William was full of expectation. I cut a fair sized chunk of ham and divided it into two. I gave William one piece and told him the other was for later. Well, he wasn't having any of that. He waited until I left the room for a few minutes. He could see the ham on the kitchen table.

Within a milli-second he had his paws on the

dining chair where he could reach the ham easily. Gulp and it was gone. He felt a little bit guilty, for taking the ham, but it was only a little bit. "WILLIAM," I shouted as I came through the door, "What have you done. Where's the ham?". He took his paws off the chair and slowly slunk back into his basket. Where he proceeded to put his paws over his nose and look up at me dolefully.

We had a family tradition of delivering our Christmas cards

An old trick. "Oh dear," I scolded, "you probably won't get any presents tomorrow now". I suppose it was partly my own fault for leaving the ham within his reach, but I wasn't going to admit that. William sulked and stayed in his basket. Eventually he fell asleep again.

We had a family tradition of delivering our Christmas cards to our neighbours at around midnight. So about eleven thirty we put on our warm coats and scarves. "Put the cards in order, so we don't have to worry about having to read the names in the dark," said Greg. So the children were happily sorting the cards, when a blurry eyed William came along to help. We must take William the children insisted. "Of course" I said. The earlier annoyance I had felt about the ham had long since disappeared. So we set off on our rounds. William wagged his tail, the children sang carols and we were a happy family team. There was however one little problem, most of our neighbours heard us coming and very kindly invited us in.

We were all tired and with full tummies

So by the time we had finished the delivery, it was shall we say, a little bit late, and we were stuffed full with sausage rolls and mince pies. The children were all full up with lemonade and Greg and I were, a little, how can I put it, VERY HAPPY!!!!, with all the toasts for a Happy Christmas we had imbibed on the way round and William had had far too many tip bits. But it was Christmas after all. We traipsed home and we were all tired and with full tummies eventually fell into bed.

In the morning when William woke up, he saw

a sack full of presents beside him. He hardly dared to hope that they were for him. Perhaps Father Christmas had not heard of yesterdays misdemeanour. He gave the sack a good sniff. "Go on open it" I said. "Yes they are all for you." With that said, wrapping paper was tossed high into the air and guess what, William had all the presents on his list. All in Red.

What a lucky Dog.

And there's more...

Much love Dottie.

William was in the car, comfortably in his seat...

The Mini

7 Dog Kennel Lane
Pidley
Cambridge
CB30 4WB

Dear Friends,

William loved going for a ride in the car. It was really good fun. He sat in the passenger seat where he could look all around him and take in the sights.

The car he liked the best was a 1968 British Racing Green Mini. Greg was a rally driver and the mini was in full competition fettle. One day he shouted, "Come on William, we'll go and test the car." He had just made some adjustments to the engine, so that it would go even faster... Before the weekend's event, he wanted to try out this latest modification.

William didn't need asking twice. He was in the car comfortably sitting in his seat before my husband had put on his driving gloves. Off they went, down the road together, 'a man and his dog'. William looked very smart in his red collar and with his head held high and his ears flapping he thought he was terribly important. I forgot to say that the weather was fairly inclement that day and as it was a late afternoon in November there was a good chance of a fog descending. They sped around the country lanes and William was having a great time . He had learned from experience to lean into the corners otherwise he fell off the seat.

He was in a small fast car, hurtling down the runway

All of a sudden the car hurtled down a small bumpy track. So not only was William holding on sideways, but now he was having to contend with bumping up and down as well. The track led down to a disused airfield where my husband often went to practice his rallying. He prided himself on being the best and definitely the fastest. I suppose by now it was about half past five, because it was fairly dark and, as expected, down came the fog. William was very unsure about this situation. He couldn't see anything. He did know, he was in a small fast car, hurtling down the runway at an alarming speed. "Well," said Greg, "the car seems to be running ok. I suppose we ought to go home for supper". William couldn't agree more. The thought of food made his mouth begin to drool. "Oh no you don't, not in my car. Wlilliam Blake!, please no". Greg opened the door and William quickly jumped out. He had a nice big shake and the drool sped off into the ether. William had a good look round. He couldn't see a paw in front of his face. He began to wonder how they were going to find the gateway off the airfield.

You really are a very clever dog

Obviously, my husband was thinking the same thing."How brave do you feel," he asked William. "I'll stay here with the car, and you go and have a look round and see if you can find the gateway. With your sense of smell you should be able to find me easily. If I go, I might be looking all night". Oh dear, thought William and I'm so hungry now,

I'll die of starvation, if I have to wait all night. So William set off on this very important mission. There were some interesting smells, he was sure there was rabbit and maybe a fox and definitely some burned rubber and fuel.

He looked back, but quite unnervingly, he couldn't see where he had left the car. Oh well, he thought, I might as well try and find the gateway. Not long after, he found it. Wow!, This was really good news.. He barked as loud as he could, to alert Greg to his location. Then he marked the gatepost, in the time honoured way, that only a dog can do. William put his head in the air took a long sniff and pinpointed the car and off he went.

And with that he ran as off as fast as he could

He found he was running. Must be the empty tummy, he thought. He quickly found Greg, who was delighted to see him and gave him a great big hug. "You really are a very clever dog William. Now come here, I am going to tie a torch to your collar, so I will be able to see you easily, whilst we find our way off the airfield". William felt so important yet again as he led my Husband off the airfield. "Jump in William, we'll see how fast we can go along the track to the main road." Oh! Oh!... thought William, bumpy up and down, sliding from side to side.

William's tummy was now registering on empty

Nope, I'm not doing that ... I'll meet you at the road, he thought and with that he ran as off as fast as he could. Obviously, the car arrived there first, but William was surprised he wasn't that far behind. Panting very hard, he jumped into his seat. William's tummy was now registering on empty. He was so pleased to be going home and to eat...

"Have I got a tale to tell you," said Greg as he came through the door... and William,... he was demolishing his supper at an alarming rate. A quick drink, a big burp, then to bed, perchance to dream of Rabbits!

And there's more...

Much love Dottie.

The people just want their sheets back..

The Thief

7 Dog Kennel Lane
Pidley
Cambridge
CB30 4WB

Dear Friends,

I have serious news, William has turned out to be a thief. It's very worrying and I'm not too sure what to do about it.

It all started when some near neighbours moved in down the road. They owned a rather odd looking dog called Twitchet. She looked like, a moth eaten rug. However, William had taken a shine to her. In fact her adored her.

One day as I came down the stairs I saw an envelope on the mat . I opened it and inside was a note. Please return in good order, one pair of men's red underpants, one green sock and one white vest. Or the bill is £5. I was totally perplexed. I showed it to Greg who couldn't shed any light on it either. I put the note to one side and went to cook the family breakfast. All the time pondering what the note could mean.

A little later in the morning, as I was hanging out the washing, I saw something red peeping through the ground. Upon investigation, I found all the items listed in the note. How very odd I thought. What should I do?... Well firstly I'll wash all the mud off and hang them out on the line.

No harm done said the neighbour

Then I'll go and have another look at the note. It said it was from No.15. So that evening, I called at the house with the nicely laundered items. "How did you know they were at my house", I asked, "Someone saw William carrying them into your garden," came the reply. "I can't apologise enough," I said. "No harm done said the neighbour". How very understanding, I thought. Turns out that William had fallen in love with Twitchet and had paid them daily, if not more visits, for the last week. I guessed he had taken the items because he wanted a token of this 'love' to bring home. At home he was an absolute pest for the next couple of weeks. In that time he brought all manner of things home, which I had to return. Then as if by magic it stopped and all was peaceful and back to normal.

A few months later, I had a feeling of deja vu when I saw something bright orange peeping through the ground in the back garden. You'll never guess what I found. Two, yes two, double, bright orange sheets.

William had again settled down and everything was peaceful

They were almost fluorescent. I dragged the muddy mess from their hiding place and put them straight into the washing machine. I was so relieved to find, that when I hung them out to dry, there were no holes or other damage. I hadn't had any notes recently from my neighbour, so I guessed that they weren't theirs. What to do I could hardly put a note in the local Post office . Found two bright orange fluorescent sheets. Surely no one would admit to owning them. So I put them in my airing cupboard whilst I thought about what I should do.

Several weeks went by and I forgot all about the sheets. William had again settled down and everything was peaceful. "William Blake, you are a naughty boy, but you are my naughty boy and I love you," I said, as I cuddled him and he returned the affection with a great big lick on the cheek.

I may be able to help you solve this serious crime

As we sat on the sofa having this nice cuddle, there was a knock on the door. On opening the door, I was a bit apprehensive, when I was confronted with the village policeman. Known to us on the quiet as Loopy Len . (I don't know to this day, if he ever knew his nick name, that he had been given by the locals). What's the matter," I said. "Can I come in", he said. "I have something of a serious nature to ask you about". I was a bit worried and racked my brain for something that either Greg or the children, or I might have done. It turned out that he had come to investigate the theft of two bright orange sheets. "Oh yes," I said, "I may be able to help you solve this serious crime". As I went upstairs to the airing cupboard, to fetch the sheets, I was thinking how on earth did he know they would be here.

When I left him in the sitting room, William was in his basket, but when I came back into the room, William was conspicuous by his absence.

The constable was very red-faced and clearly not amused

I nervously asked," How did you know they would be here," Loopy Len replied, "I have been talking to the people at No.15 and they suggested that I try here. I handed over the neatly laundered bright orange sheets. With this serious crime solved, Loopy Len stood up ready to leave."You won't be hearing any more of this matter," he said. "The people won't press charges, they just want their sheets back." By this time I was stifling my laughter, when all of a sudden, I realised that Loopy Len was looking for his hat. "I'm sure I put it on the table," he said. Oh no! surely not, "William Blake!, what have you done now.?"... I rushed out into the garden, just as William was about to dispatch the hat into the ground. I grabbed the hat off him and brushed off the dirt. Coming back into the sitting room, the constable was very red-faced and clearly not amused. "Get that dog under control"! he yelled, as I opened the door for him to leave.

I was beside myself with laughter. I turned on William, I was going to give him a piece of my mind, but I couldn't do it, because I just fell about laughing every time I looked at him.

When the family came home, I told them about the day's events and they all fell about laughing too.

"We need to sort this problem out," I spluttered "Any ideas anyone?"

And there's more...

Much love Dottie.

The Birthday

7 Dog Kennel Lane
Pidley
Cambridge
CB30 4WB

Dear Friends,

William's birthday was on November 14th. The children thought it would be good to celebrate the occasion with a party. They began making the arrangements on bonfire night.

We had invited the neighbours to our house and garden, for a bonfire, fireworks, eats and drinks gathering. I must admit I hadn't expected quite so many to take up our offer, but nevertheless a good time was had by all. We all crammed into No.7 and everyone contributed towards the festivities.

William was pleasantly surprise by the attention...

Unbeknown to my husband and I, the children had a captive audience for inviting people to William's birthday party, not only did they invite a lot of people, but told them they could bring their pets too. They didn't specify what type of pets would be welcome, so you can understand my apprehension when I found out, that this was in fact, the situation. During the next nine days there was a lot of whispering in corners and lots of "I need more money for William's party."

They made him a breakfast of boiled egg and soldiers

I was intrigued by what was going on, but when I asked about how things were going, I was told it was top secret and I would find out on the day. Not wishing to spoil their fun, I resisted asking for more details.

Eventually the day arrived and William was pleasantly surprised by all the attention he was getting. First thing in the morning, before he was out of his bed he was presented with a saucer of tea and a biscuit, What a treat, he thought, I could get used to this. However, I was thinking, I hope this isn't setting a precedence for the future.

Then the children sat him on a chair at the table. They made him a breakfast of boiled egg and soldiers, Matt dipped the soldiers into the egg and Vicky fed them to William. Again the thought went through my mind, I hope this isn't setting a new beginning to William's day.

Later that morning the children set about getting the party ready, they had been very busy during the past few days and I wondered what might lie ahead.

Sparky yapped for all he was worth

I began to feel slightly nervous when I saw on the table a range of pet foods. From dog treats, hamster treats, nuts for the birds, to something quite revolting for a snake and so on. When they brought out a bag of oats for the pony, I thought they were winding me up. "Godfathers, are you sure all these animals are coming", I said. "Oh yes", said my daughter", we've had all the replies."

The first to arrive was Sparky, the dog from next door, William was stunned, not that noisy, grumpy dog that I hate, the one that scratched my nose. William growled and showed his teeth, Sparky yapped for all he was worth, I'm not sure what they were saying to each other but it certainly wasn't polite. The children looked very worried, "I know, I'll give them a bone each" said Matt " perhaps they'll be good then," well eventually they settled down, keeping a wary eye on each other all the time.

William loved unwrapping presents

More of the animals and their owners started arriving, it was a bit like Noah's Ark. The children offered the appropriate treats to each animal and sandwiches and cake to their owners. All seemed to be going well, even William and Sparky were tolerating each other.

The pony called Twinkle had been left outside. So he didn't feel left out of the party, the children put on their coats and went outside to give him a hug and the bag of oats. They decided this would be a good time to give William his present. My son brought out a very large box all wrapped up in brown paper. Written on the side of the box was 'To William Blake, our bestest ever friend, with lots of love from your family'. William loved unwrapping presents. He loved the noise the paper made as he tore it off. With paper tossed high in the air he eventually, found inside the box an assortment of gifts. A red ball, a chewy stick, a box of dog biscuits and a squeaky toy. William was thrilled with all these new presents especially the squeaky toy. All I could think of was how quickly he could get the squeaker out of the toy. It made a deafening, horrible sound, in fact it took him all of a minute to dispatch it to where it couldn't be heard. What a relief.

A succession of animals either on leads, being carried or in cages

Eventually it was time to bring the party to a close. Everyone had enjoyed themselves and started to leave. I have often wondered what people passing by might have thought seeing a succession of animals either on leads, being carried or in cages and the pony clip-clopping his way out. Maybe the slightly eccentric family from No.7 would have been the kindest thought. When the children started planning the party for the next year I tried to think of a reason why they shouldn't, I'm still thinking.

And there's more...
Much love Dottie.

A Wagon Wheel, his favorite treat...

Down the Road

7 Dog Kennel Lane
Pidley
Cambridge
CB30 4WB

Dear Friends,

Just down the road from No.7, about half a mile, was a very busy factory. They made glue and glued structures together and things like that. The work force were hard working people, many of whom were our neighbour's. The men were always ready for their breaks and especially the lunch break.

This may have been because of the local entertainment that occurred. They gathered round to chat and eat their sandwiches and drink lots and lots of coffee. "Here he comes," said one of the workmen. "I wonder how he knows it's lunch time." Who should appear at the gate, but William

Blake. He dug his heels in and came to a halt just level with the opening in the gate. He had a big shake and sauntered over to the men. William had a peculiar habit of pulling up his top lip to grin, when he was after something "There's no need to look like Mr. Super Cool, we know you've been running to get here, before we have eaten all our lunches". William pulled back his lip again and eyed up the lunch boxes and started to drool "Oh no", one of the men said and handed over a sandwich very quickly.

He wriggled up his nose and showed his teeth again

"It's a horrid habit you've got there Mr.Blake" William wasn't the least bit fazed by this comment, and stared intently at another lunch box. To divert his attention, another of the men, said loudly, so everyone could hear, "Do you know what Williams nick name is," ...It's Willy Bumble."... William was horrified, he didn't know it was common knowledge. He wriggled up his nose and showed his teeth again. "What a soppy look" said the man and all of them started to laugh. William put up with this teasing, because he knew he would get a sandwich in the end. He hated being laughed at, but he would tolerate almost anything, if the reward was something to eat. "How about going up on the lift?', said one of the men. The lift was just a flat platform with stairs running up on one side of it. William scampered up the stairs and looked down. Ooh ..it was a long way down. He carefully stepped onto the lift and almost immediately he was going down.

William instantly sat down and looked up at him pleadingly

He jumped off the lift just before it reached the bottom. Wagging his tail, he ran over to the men for his reward...a sandwich. He thought what a good game and ran over to the stairs and climed to the top again. Carefully stepping onto the lift just as the lift began to go down. William realised he could see right into the lunch boxes down below. He was sure he recognized the wrapper of a Wagon Wheel, his favorite treat. When the lift was low enough for him to jump off William ran full tilt up to the man who had the Wagon Wheel. "Sit," said the man and William instantly sat down and looked up at him pleadingly, with his big brown eyes. 'Oh! you really know how to turn on the charm," the man said. William wriggled his nose. I've had plenty of practice he thought to himself. The man reached in to his box and brought out a lovely ham sandwich. William had a quick chew and then swallowed it whole. All the time he was staring at the lunch box.

What a good lunch time that turned out to be

Then he barked and looked intently at the box with the Wagon Wheel inside. The man pulled it out. Woof, Woof, Woof, Woof, barked William and wagged his tail very hard. "This clever dog has just asked me for my Wagon Wheel," the man said, in utter amazement. "Well I can hardly refuse can I" he said to William. "Here you are, I'll share it with you. Half each." The men all laughed and agreed William was the cleverest dog they knew. William gave the man a big lick and turned to make his way home. Well, what a good lunch time that turned out to be, thought William. "See you tomorrow," called the men. "We look forward to your visits Willy Bumble". William turned and wriggled up his nose... *If I can escape again, I most definitely will*, thought William.

Unfortunately, big black clouds had started forming and there was a bright flash of thunder. *Oh no*, thought William *I'm going to get wet. Very, very wet.*

The most beautiful rainbow hung there

Something he hated. It just so happened that the village shop was on his way home, so he headed for the door way, at an alarming rate. Coming to an abrupt halt level with the doorway, he was just about to shelter, when he realized there was someone already in there. It was a little girl and she was sobbing her heart out. She looked very frightened. William squeezed in beside her and gave her a big lick. She started to stroke Williams head and gradually she stopped crying. She wasn't frightened anymore, not now she had William to cuddle. Eventually, the rain stopped. The little girl pointed to the sky. The most beautiful rainbow hung there. It was a complete one. "Do you know, spotty dog, if you can find the end of the rainbow, you'll find a pot of gold. That's what my mother told me". William nuzzled against her and licked her face. "It's time to go home", she said, so with William trotting beside her off they went. When they reached the gateway to her house, she gave William a big hug and whispered in his ear, "I wish you were my dog".

"William Blake! where have you been. I have been very worried," I said . "You are so naughty, going out on your own. You've been gone ages." William sloped off to his bed. He put his paws over his nose and looked up at me with his big brown eyes. I just hope you haven't got into any mischief whilst you've been out." I said. I knew what he was thinking

I could see the expression on his face. It's for me to know and you to wonder about...

And there's more...

In the next misdemeanours of William Blake

Much love Dottie.

ACKNOWLEDGEMENTS

I have many people to thank for helping me along the way, from those who have patiently either read or listened to the stories, your encouragement has been heart warming.

Haley for drawing the lovely pictures. Sally, Richard, Debbie, John and Tricia, Eileen, Tracy, Derek and Leslie, Penny and Pauline for helping me with the edits, and Jon for the typesetting. Jayne, Anne and Tracy for their helpful contributions and for all the people to whom I have read the stories and their encouragement to bring my work to print.

For my grandchildren, Tristan, Leon and Freya for whom I signed their cards with the thumb print of William, and my mother who taught me to draw round my thumb to make a dogs head when I was very young.

My dear mother for whom I wrote these stories.

Thank you.
Much love Dottie.